HISTOIRE

The Acadiana area is comprised of 22 parishes in south Louisiana. Originally, it included eight parishes: Acadia, Evangeline, Iberia, Lafayette, Saint Landry, Saint Martin, Saint Mary and Vermilion. Fourteen more were added recently and now Acadiana extends from the Texas border to the parish of Avoyelles to the north, Lafourche parish to the east and the Gulf of Mexico to the south. A true "gumbo pot" of people makes this part of the state unique. The catch phrase of Lafayette is "Genuine Cajun. Uniquely Creole." Acadian French heritage is so rich that many still speak French or Cajun French today. When the French Acadians settled here over 200 years ago, they added a wealth of cultural traditions to Native American, African and Spanish lifestyles. They built their homes along the bayous of south central and south western Louisiana and the Vermilion River. The area became known as Vermilionville. In 1844, in honor of the French Marquis de Lafayette, who defended the colonies during the American Revolutionary War, it was renamed Lafayette—the Heart of Acadiana. Unofficially, it is the capital of Cajun Country.

Acadians are fond of saying "*Laissez le bon temps rouler*" which means "Let the good times roll." Around here that's just what we do! We celebrate everything with Cajun food, Zydeco music and, most importantly, spicy people!

Au revoir, bonne nuit and bonne lecture!

ISBN 978-1-4507-9590-6

Design
David Robson, Robson Design

Published by
AMPERSAND, INC.
1050 North State Street
Chicago, IL 60610

203 Finland Place
New Orleans, LA 70113
www.ampersandworks.com

Printed in Canada

To arrange a reading or book signing,
contact the author at
www.GoodnightAcadiana.com

Goodnight ACADIANA

Written by Lesley Crawford Costner

Illustrated by Camille Barnes

AMP&RSAND, INC.

Chicago • New Orleans

*To all southwestern Louisiana
residents who make me proud
to be from the South. To my parents
and my husband who think that
I can do anything, when really
I can do nothing without them.
Je vous aime!*

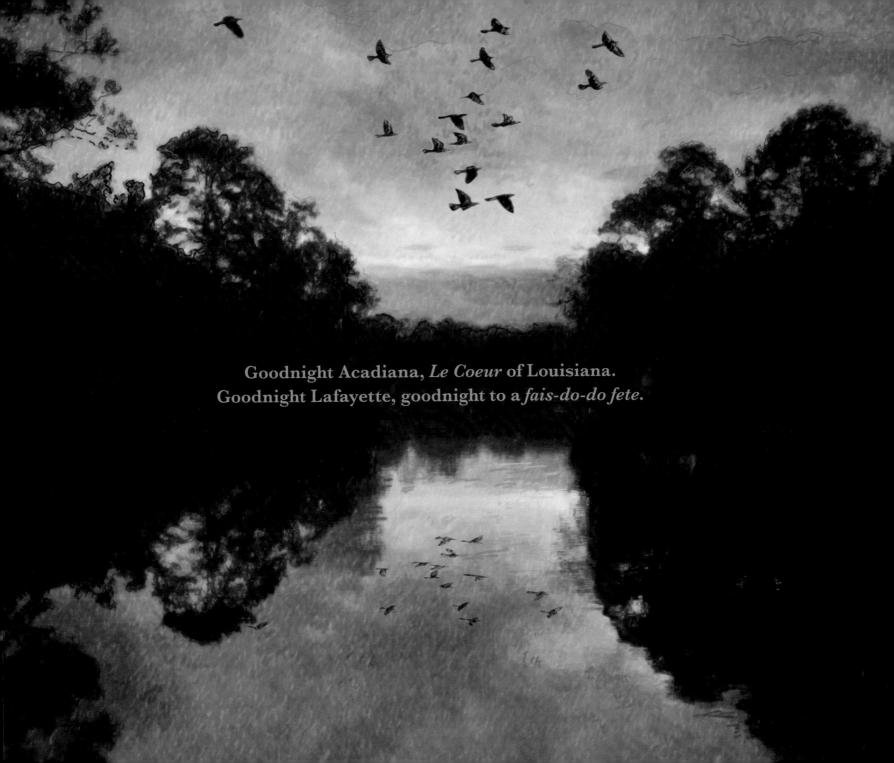

Goodnight Acadiana, *Le Coeur* of Louisiana.
Goodnight Lafayette, goodnight to a *fais-do-do fete.*

Goodnight Henderson Swamp and moss draped cypress trees,
Where you can ogle alligators if you please.

Goodnight La Fonda, Don's and Prejean's, too.
Goodnight *écrevisse* and Cajun spices for our *roux*.

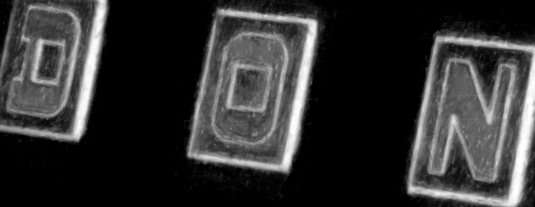

Goodnight Cajun Field and the famous Cajundome.
Ice Gators and Ragin' Cajuns® call these places home.

Goodnight Vermilion River. Goodnight Bayou Teche.
Goodnight Cajun waters. Goodnight *poisson*, so fresh!

Goodnight Saint John *Cathédrale*, where we fold our hands to pray.
Goodnight Blue Dog paintings in the famed Blue Dog *Café*.

Goodnight black bear, at home in the Atchafalaya.
Goodnight seafood gumbo, *boudin* and jambalaya.

EVANGELINE OA

Meeting place of Evang
& Gabriel whose counterp
Emmeline Labiche and
Arcenaux, lived here. Re
of his home is in Longf
Evangeline State Park
mile N. Evangeline's
is at the rear of chu

Goodnight to all Native American tribes.
Goodnight Evangeline Oak, and goodnight to love that thrives.

Goodnight Children's Museum. Goodnight Planetarium.
Goodnight *les enfants*. Tomorrow you'll learn, play and run.

Goodnight Blackham Coliseum. Goodnight rodeo.
Goodnight Avery Island's TABASCO.® Goodnight Zydeco.

Goodnight fried cracklings at the famous _Boucherie_.
Goodnight Cajun stories of the pirate Jean Lafitte.

Goodnight Acadian Village and this here's a fact...
For those of you just visiting, we sure hope y'all come back!

Bonne Nuit

Lagniappe

Acadiana–named for the Acadians who settled in Louisiana after their French colony in Canada was overtaken by the British in the 1700–1800s.

Acadian Village–located in Lafayette, a replica of Acadian homes and heritage of the 1800s.

American Alligator–the largest reptile in North America. Over two million of them live in Louisiana.

Atchafalaya Basin–the largest swamp in the United States. Native American word for "long river."

Avery Island–serene piece of land surrounded by marsh and swamps where moss-covered oak trees provide shade, pepper fields grow and snowy white egrets are protected. Home of McIlhenny Company's TABASCO® Sauce.

Bayou–a flat, low-lying area like a swamp, but it moves! From the Choctaw "*bayuk*" for creek.

Bayou Teche–home to the American Alligator and Louisiana Black Bear which are now endangered species.

Blackham Coliseum–built in 1949 to hold 9,800 Cajuns!

Blue Dog *Café*–delicious Cajun food and displays of artwork of Cajun culture and the iconic Blue Dog.

Boucherie–French, meaning a slaughtering of pigs at a place where families can process ham, pork chops, sausage and head cheese to have plenty of food for cold winter months.

Boudin–French, meaning a link sausage made of pork, pork liver and rice mixed with Creole seasonings.

Cajun–a descendent of the Acadians.

Cajundome–completed in 1985, it supports community concerts, sports events, conventions and other special events.

Children's Museum of Acadiana–a non-profit organization resulting from the vision of three women–Renee Miller, Mitzi Domino and Marvita Hudson. Geaux Girls!

Cracklings–the crisp, brown bits of pork left after the fat of the pig has been rendered.

Crawfish–if you live in Louisiana, you know how to boil this freshwater crustacean.

Creole–people of any race or mixture descended from French and Spanish settlers.

Don's Restaurant–opened in 1934 as a beer parlor and grew into a very successful seafood and steak house.

Écrevisse–French, meaning crawfish.

Evangeline Oak–immortalizes exile of Emmeline Labiche and Louis Arceneaux from Nova Scotia in 1755–Longfellow's inspiration for Evangeline and Gabriel who fell in love under this tree.

Fais-do-do–Cajun festival where adults can dance after the children fall asleep. From old French: "*fais*" meaning to carry out; do-do from "*dormir*," meaning to sleep.

Fleur de lis–old French, meaning "flower of the Lily"–a symbol of many royal families and of the Holy Family.

Gumbo–a spicy chicken or seafood stew served with rice, from the Bantu word "*ngombo*" meaning okra.

Henderson Swamp–over 1.2 million acres in the Atchafalaya Basin; home to over 300 species of wildlife.

Ice Gators Hockey Team–began in 1995 in the ECHL and is now part of the Southern Professional Hockey League.

Jambalaya–inspired by Spanish cooking, a dish of chicken, sausage, rice, onions, celery and tomatoes mixed with Cajun spices. The name comes from French "*jambalaia*."

Lafayette Science Museum–over 10,000 sq. ft. of exhibitions featuring hands-on science and a planetarium.